This book is dedicated to:

DAILY ♥ JOURNAL

FRIENDS

WIND OF WISHES ♥
AN INSPIRATIONAL GUIDED JOURNAL

© 2001 Havoc Publishing
San Diego, California
U.S.A.

Artwork © 2001 Teresa Kogut
Text © Amy Spitler

ISBN 0-7416-1918-0

www.havocpub.com

Made in Korea

Birth Information

Family Memories

Childhood

Significant Moments

Precious Memories

Today and Tomorrow

Dreams and Wishes

Sharing is Important

Lessons Learned

Heartfelt Pride

Record Keeping —

THE CHAIN OF LOVE

Birth Information

My Given Name:

My Birth Date:

Place of Birth (City, State, County, Country):

Weight:

Length:

I was this kind of baby...

When sharing her story
It is a grandmother's goal
To paint a picture for her loved ones
That is both charming and whole.

This is a special story about the day that I was born...

_____

_____

_____

_____

_____

My parents decided to name me after...

_____

_____

_____

_____

_____

_____

_____

Some important events of the time were...

_____

_____

_____

_____

Baby Picture

THE PEOPLE we share our lives with and lend a helping hand, are not just lucky happenstance, yet a mystery in GOD'S PLAN

Family Memories

I am the daughter of:...

I was named after...

I look like...

We all come from somewhere
Our stories entwined
A product of the lives
Of our ancestors combined

My mother's parents were...

_____

_____

_____

_____

My father's family was...

_____

_____

_____

I will share a story about my grandparents

_____

_____

_____

When I think about my mother, I am always amazed at the way she...

_____

_____

_____

_____

_____

_____

_____

_____

_____

In my life, my father always represents...

_____

_____

_____

_____

_____

_____

_____

I am the sibling of...

My siblings were my partners in...

I remember...

I cherish the memory of when my family...

This is the story of a large family gathering...

Some important facts about my family history...

_____

_____

_____

_____

My ancestors came from...

_____

_____

_____

_____

_____

_____

They worked as...

_____

_____

_____

_____

♥ Family Photo Gallery ♥

Childhood

My youth was filled with magic
As I learned to find my way in this world
And discovered the blessings of my life
Lying before me unfurled

A description of my childhood home...

_____

_____

_____

The area where I lived was...

_____

_____

_____

I lived there until I was...

_____

_____

_____

We had a family pet named...

_____

_____

_____

When I think about my neighborhood, I miss...

My close friend _____ and I used to love to...

One toy that was special to me was my...

I went to school at:

I remember a special teacher who made me feel...

I loved to learn about...

I wish I had paid closer attention to...

Angels In My Life
RECORD BOOK
Sisters

As a teenager, I loved to...

_____

_____

_____

_____

_____

Driving was a privilege that I...

_____

_____

_____

_____

_____

_____

The first person I had a crush on was...

_____

_____

_____

_____

A special vacation memory with my family was...

_____

_____

_____

_____

_____

_____

In the summer I spent my time...

_____

_____

_____

_____

_____

_____

_____

I remember going to...

_____

_____

_____

_____

_____

It left an impression on me because...

_____

_____

_____

_____

_____

_____

The farthest place I have traveled to is...

_____

_____

_____

_____

_____

♥♥ Photo Gallery ♥♥

♥ Significant Moments ♥

We earmark our lives with experiences that are profound
And turn back the pages of the book of life we have bound

remember when man first walked on the moon. If I could have written part of Neil Armstrong's
speech, I would have told the world...

_____
_____
_____
_____
_____
_____
_____
_____
_____
_____
_____
_____
_____
_____
_____

I will never forget the day that...

_____

_____

_____

_____

_____

_____

As a teenager, my idea of the world was shaped by a particular event...

_____

_____

_____

I will always remember where I was the day...

_____

_____

In my lifetime, I have seen amazing things. Our society has advanced in so many ways. These are some of the most significant discoveries or events in my lifetime and how I feel about them:

Scientific:

_____
_____
_____
_____

Medical:

_____
_____
_____

Historical:

_____
_____
_____

Political:

_____
_____

Personal:

_____
_____
_____

If I could change the course of events from the past in one way, it would be to...

_____

_____

_____

_____

_____

_____

The world has changed the most in my lifetime by...

_____

_____

_____

_____

_____

_____

_____

_____

Photo Gallery

⭐ Precious Memories ⭐

This is the story of how I met my husband...

_____

_____

_____

_____

_____

_____

_____

Our courtship began...

_____

_____

_____

_____

_____

_____

_____

_____

Falling in love was...

_____

_____

_____

_____

_____

We were married on...

_____

_____

_____

_____

_____

We shared dreams of...

_____

_____

_____

_____

_____

Our wedding day was...

_____

_____

_____

_____

A tender memory about being a mother that I treasure is...

_____

_____

_____

_____

_____

_____

I am proud of myself for...

_____

_____

_____

_____

_____

_____

_____

The traditions of my childhood holidays were...

_____

_____

_____

_____

_____

_____

_____

I remember my grandmother sharing...

_____

_____

_____

_____

_____

_____

_____

_____

Photograph of Grandmother/Grandfather

⭐ Today and Tomorrow ⭐

A wise person once told me to make the most of each day
To cherish the little things as we go on our way

Some of my favorite things to do are...

_____

_____

_____

_____

_____

_____

I always seem to smile when...

_____

_____

_____

_____

_____

_____

_____

When I am alone, I find time to...

_____

_____

_____

I love to collect...

_____

_____

_____

_____

If I had to choose a favorite musician, singer or composer, I would choose...

_____

_____

_____

_____

A song that is special to me is... _____ because...

_____

_____

_____

BABY

School Days

When I read, I choose books about...

_____

_____

_____

_____

_____

Writing for me is...

_____

_____

_____

_____

An author I admire would be...

_____

_____

_____

A children's book I love to share is...

_____

_____

_____

GRANDMOTHERS

have already

earned their wings

Dreams and Wishes

Dreams and wishes will become reality
When we commit ourselves to the future and set our minds free.

As a child I dreamed of becoming...

_____

_____

_____

_____

_____

_____

_____

_____

I remember thinking about the future and wondering...

_____

_____

_____

_____

_____

_____

_____

_____

When I became a mother, I wished for my children...

_____

_____

_____

_____

For my grandchildren's lives, I hope...

_____

_____

_____

_____

_____

_____

One thing that I would like to accomplish in the future is to...

_____

_____

_____

_____

_____

A dream I am currently making come true is...

_____

_____

_____

If I could ensure one thing for future generations it would be...

_____

_____

_____

I would like to live long enough to see...

_____

_____

_____

_____

When I look at my life, I know that my wishes have come true because...

_____

_____

_____

To me, dreams and wishes are a way to express...

_____

_____

_____

♥ Sharing is Important ♥

If I were to choose a family recipe to share, it would be...

_____

_____

_____

_____

_____

_____

_____

_____

_____

Tradition to me means...

_____

_____

_____

_____

_____

_____

Sharing is Important
For without each other we would be
Alone without the benefit
of another's company

When I want to share in my relatives' past I...

_____

_____

_____

_____

_____

_____

_____

I get sentimental about...

_____

_____

_____

_____

_____

_____

I show my appreciation for the people I love by...

_____
_____
_____
_____
_____
_____
_____
_____
_____

I share in the experiences of my friends in order to...

_____
_____
_____
_____
_____
_____
_____
_____
_____

Sharing quiet moments with my grandchildren allows me to...

_____

_____

_____

_____

_____

_____

_____

With my children and grandchildren, I would like to share...

_____

_____

_____

_____

_____

_____

_____

Photo Gallery

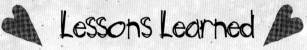

Lessons Learned

I believe that some important things about life are...

_____

_____

_____

Marriage...

_____

_____

_____

Raising Children...

_____

_____

_____

Friendship...

_____

_____

Self-Truth...

_____

_____

_____

PEACE

JOY

HoPE

LOVE

I would characterize my life as one filled with...

_____

_____

_____

_____

_____

I would like to think that I have influenced others by...

_____

_____

_____

_____

_____

_____

_____

_____

_____

_____

My mother always taught me to...

_____

_____

_____

_____

_____

I have learned from my children to...

_____

_____

_____

_____

_____

_____

_____

PEACE

JOY

A person that I admire and hope to be like is...

because...

I have learned to be thankful for...

HOPE

LOVE

PEACE

JOY

I am still learning about the importance of...

in my life...

The lessons I see repeating themselves in my life are...

HOPE

Reverence

LOVE

My heart sings with joy
While my soul is filled with glory
At the accomplishments
that surround me
And embellish my life's story

PEACE

♥ Heartfelt Pride ♥

I take pride in my children's ability to...

_____

_____

_____

_____

_____

_____

_____

My grandchildren are my pride and joy because...

_____

_____

_____

_____

_____

_____

People know they can count on me to...

_____

_____

_____

_____

_____

_____

They describe me as...

_____

_____

_____

_____

_____

_____

_____

_____

_____

_____

_____

_____

Gratitude

Compassion

My family has always taken pride in the achievement of a relative who...

_____

_____

_____

_____

_____

_____

_____

_____

A person that I am honored to have in my family is...

_____

_____

_____

_____

_____

_____

_____

_____

My favorite thing to brag about is...

_____

_____

_____

_____

_____

_____

I was the first person in my family to...

_____

_____

_____

_____

_____

_____

_____

_____

_____

I am proud of myself for...

_____

_____

_____

_____

_____

_____

I see myself as a person who is...

_____

_____

_____

_____

_____

_____

_____

_____

♥ Record Keeping ♥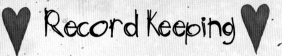

Births and Deaths (names and dates)
_____
_____
_____
_____
_____

Marriages and Important Events (dates)
_____
_____
_____
_____
_____

Celebrations
_____
_____
_____
_____

Political and Social Events
_____
_____
_____
_____